Best Friends

Learning Simple Shapes

SCHOLASTIC

Hints About Shapes

Learning to identify shapes trains your child's eye to later identify letters and words. The best friends in this book are a circle, square, and triangle. What happens in the story when a circle is squeezed? It turns into an oval. A square squashes into a rectangle. A triangle stays a triangle, even when it is upside down. Explore these ideas with your child.

Ask for Bob Books at your local bookstore, or visit www.bobbooks.com

No part of this publication may be reproduced, stored in a retrieval system, or transmitted in any form or by any means, electronic, mechanical, photocopying, recording, or otherwise, without written permission of the publisher. For information regarding permission, write to Scholastic Inc. Attention: Permissions Department, 557 Broadway, New York, NY 10012.

ISBN 10: 0-545-06491-0
ISBN 13: 978-0-545-06491-0

30 29 28   21 22/0
Printed in China
First printing. August 2008

Best Friends
Learning Simple Shapes

by Lynn Maslen Kertell
pictures by Sue Hendra and John R. Maslen

Scholastic Inc.
New York • Toronto • London • Auckland • Sydney • Mexico City • New Delhi • Hong Kong • Buenos Aires

Sally, a circle, was best friends
with a square named Seth.

Wherever Sally went, Seth went too.
Whatever Sally liked, Seth liked too.

One day, a triangle named Tanner
moved in next door. Soon Sally, Seth,
and Tanner were three good friends.

4

Until one morning, Sally liked one thing, but Seth and Tanner liked something different.

Sally felt sad. She gave
herself a sorry hug.

Seth and Tanner searched for Sally,
but she was no longer a circle. Her
friends didn't recognize her.

Seth and Tanner missed Sally. Seth slumped down. Tanner was upset.

All three started to cry, and out came tears shaped like squares, triangles, and circles.

When Sally saw the shapes of the tear
she laughed until she felt she would
burst. And look! She was a circle again

When Seth and Tanner saw her,
they perked up and giggled too.

Sally, Seth, and Tanner
were themselves again—
three good friends.

The Complete Bob Books® Series

READING READINESS

MY FIRST
BOB BOOKS ®
PRE-READING
SKILLS

MY FIRST
BOB BOOKS ®
ALPHABET

STAGE 1: STARTING TO READ

SET 1
BEGINNING
READERS

FIRST
STORIES

RHYMING
WORDS

STAGE 2: EMERGING READER

SET 2
ADVANCING
BEGINNERS

SIGHT WORDS
KINDERGARTEN

SIGHT WORDS
FIRST GRADE

STAGE 3: DEVELOPING READER

SET 3
WORD
FAMILIES

SET 4
COMPLEX
WORDS

SET 5
LONG
VOWELS

Lexile® Measure: AD530L
Guided Reading Level: I
Scholastic Reading Level: 2
Word Count: 153

Bob Books Apps
are available for
phones & tablets

www.BobBooks.com

Scholastic Inc
978-0-545-064

Hide-and-seek

Finding Hidden Shapes

My First
BOB
BOOKS

Hints About Hidden Shapes

Look for Sally, Seth, and Tanner playing hide-and-seek in this book.
Can your child find the other circles, squares, and triangles?
Continue the game throughout your house. How many squares
can you find? How many circles? How many different shapes can
your child identify in one room?

ISBN 10: 0-545-06492-9
ISBN 13: 978-0-545-06492-7

30 29 28   21 22/0
Printed in China
First printing. August 2008

Hide-and-seek

Finding Hidden Shapes

by Lynn Maslen Kertell
pictures by Sue Hendra and John R. Maslen

Scholastic Inc.
New York • Toronto • London • Auckland • Sydney • Mexico City • New Delhi • Hong Kong • Buenos Aires

Seth, Tanner, and Sally were
best friends. They liked
to play hide-and-seek.

"I'm It! I'm It!" shouted Sally.
Tanner and Seth ran to hide.

3

"Where is Seth? Where is he?"
thought Sally. She looked and looked.

4

"Can't find me," called Seth.

"Where is Tanner? Where is he?"
asked Sally and Seth.

They looked and looked.
"Come and get me," teased Tanner.

"My turn to hide!" said Sally.
"Where is Sally? Where is she?"
wondered Seth and Tanner.

"Here I am," laughed Sally.

9

Sally, Seth, and Tanner all hid.

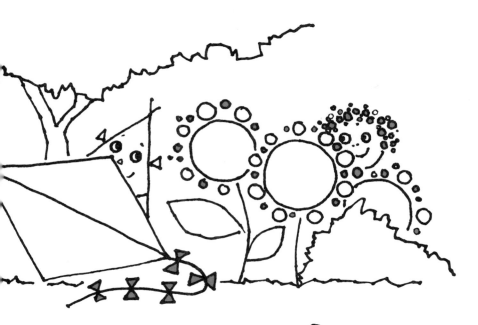

Where did they go?

Here they are!

The Complete Bob Books® Series

READING READINESS

MY FIRST BOB BOOKS® PRE-READING SKILLS

MY FIRST BOB BOOKS® ALPHABET

STAGE 1: STARTING TO READ

SET 1 BEGINNING READERS

FIRST STORIES

RHYMING WORDS

STAGE 2: EMERGING READER

SET 2 ADVANCING BEGINNERS

SIGHT WORDS KINDERGARTEN

SIGHT WORDS FIRST GRADE

STAGE 3: DEVELOPING READER

SET 3 WORD FAMILIES

SET 4 COMPLEX WORDS

SET 5 LONG VOWELS

Lexile® Measure: AD120L
Guided Reading Level: F
Scholastic Reading Level: 1
Word Count: 97

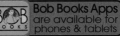

Bob Books Apps are available for phones & tablets

www.BobBooks.com

Scholastic Inc
978-0-545-064

The Picnic

Matching Shapes

Hints About Matching Shapes

What do Sally's favorite foods have in common? (They're all round.) What other shapes match in this book? Once the shapes get mixed up, can your child figure out which food went with which character? Cut sandwiches and fruit into shapes, so your children can "eat circles, squares, and triangles."

Ask for Bob Books at your local bookstore, or visit www.bobbooks.com

ISBN 10: 0-545-06493-7
ISBN 13: 978-0-545-06493-4

30 29 28   21 22/0
Printed in China
First printing. August 2008

The Picnic
Matching Shapes

by Lynn Maslen Kertell
pictures by Sue Hendra and John R. Maslen

Scholastic Inc.
New York • Toronto • London • Auckland • Sydney • Mexico City • New Delhi • Hong Kong • Buenos Aires

What a day for a picnic! Sally and
her brother, Mat, went to the park.

Seth took his brother Mac. Tanner
took his brother Sam and sister Dot.

3

Mat and Sally brought their favorite

foods — grapes, oranges, and plums.

Mac and Seth packed peanut-
butter-and-jelly sandwiches.

6

Sam, Tanner, and Dot cut up
pizza and pie for the picnic.

Tanner asked, "Pizza, anyone?"
Sally said, "Who likes fruit?"

"Please have sandwiches, too!"
exclaimed Seth.

Seth, Sally, and Tanner
sat down to eat.

What a yummy lunch!

They had lots of fun eating
circles, squares, and triangles.

The Complete Bob Books® Series

READING READINESS

MY FIRST
BOB BOOKS®
PRE-READING
SKILLS

MY FIRST
BOB BOOKS®
ALPHABET

STAGE 1: STARTING TO READ

SET 1
BEGINNING
READERS

FIRST
STORIES

RHYMING
WORDS

STAGE 2: EMERGING READER

SET 2
ADVANCING
BEGINNERS

SIGHT WORDS
KINDERGARTEN

SIGHT WORDS
FIRST GRADE

STAGE 3: DEVELOPING READER

SET 3
WORD
FAMILIES

SET 4
COMPLEX
WORDS

SET 5
LONG
VOWELS

Lexile® Measure: AD510L
Guided Reading Level: G
Scholastic Reading Level: 2
Word Count: 94

 Bob Books Apps
are available for
phones & tablets

www.BobBooks.com

Scholastic Inc
978-0-545-064

The Mix-up

Learning Simple Sorting

SCHOLASTIC

My First
BOB
BOOKS

Hints About Sorting

This book focuses on categories. Tanner likes things that roll.
Ask your child, "What is the same about things that roll? What
do they have in common?" Your child can look through the
pile of toys in the book to find things that roll. Then discuss
what toy animals have in common. What about blocks?

Ask for Bob Books at your local bookstore, or visit www.bobbooks.com

No part of this publication may be reproduced, stored in a retrieval system, or transmitted in any form
or by any means, electronic, mechanical, photocopying, recording, or otherwise, without written
permission of the publisher. For information regarding permission, write to Scholastic Inc.
Attention: Permissions Department, 557 Broadway, New York, NY 10012.

ISBN 10: 0-545-06505-4
ISBN 13: 978-0-545-06505-4

Copyright © 2008 by Lynn Maslen Kertell. All rights reserved. Published by Scholastic Inc. by arrangement
with Bob Books ® New Initiatives LLC. SCHOLASTIC and associated logos are trademarks and/or registered
trademarks of Scholastic Inc. BOB BOOKS and MY FIRST BOB BOOKS are trademarks and/or registered
trademarks of Bob Books Publications LLC.

30 29 28   21 22/0
Printed in China
First printing. August 2008

The Mix-up
Learning Simple Sorting

by Lynn Maslen Kertell
pictures by Sue Hendra and John R. Maslen

Scholastic Inc.
New York • Toronto • London • Auckland • Sydney • Mexico City • New Delhi • Hong Kong • Buenos Aires

Sally, Seth, and Tanner wanted
to build a toy village.

2

"But how?" said Sally,
looking at the jumbled pile of toys.

3

Tanner liked toys that rolled.

He wanted to find all the
cars, trucks, and tractors.

Sally was looking for animals.

She found a few.
Where were the others?

7

Seth wanted to make the buildings.

He needed to find all the blocks.

They found their favorite toys.

They were ready to build!

The trucks, animals, and blocks
made an excellent village!

The Complete Bob Books® Series

READING READINESS

MY FIRST
BOB BOOKS®
PRE-READING
SKILLS

MY FIRST
BOB BOOKS®
ALPHABET

STAGE 1: STARTING TO READ

SET 1
BEGINNING
READERS

FIRST
STORIES

RHYMING
WORDS

STAGE 2: EMERGING READER

SET 2
ADVANCING
BEGINNERS

SIGHT WORDS
KINDERGARTEN

SIGHT WORDS
FIRST GRADE

STAGE 3: DEVELOPING READER

SET 3
WORD
FAMILIES

SET 4
COMPLEX
WORDS

SET 5
LONG
VOWELS

Lexile® Measure: AD400L
Guided Reading Level: F
Scholastic Reading Level: 1
Word Count: 81

Bob Books Apps
are available for
phones & tablets

www.BobBooks.com

Scholastic In
978-0-545-065

Fix It!

Matching and Sorting

My First
BOB
BOOKS

Hints About More Complex Sorting

This book helps kids learn what things go together, sorting by shape and function. Sally needs a round top for her broken drum. Seth needs a stick to fly his flag. Tanner needs a round wheel to fix his tricycle. Give your child plenty of time as she contemplates the different choices. Considering all the possibilities can be educational (and fun) for your youngster. For example, how would the tricycle work with a square tire?

Ask for Bob Books at your local bookstore, or visit www.bobbooks.com

No part of this publication may be reproduced, stored in a retrieval system, or transmitted in any form or by any means, electronic, mechanical, photocopying, recording, or otherwise, without written permission of the publisher. For information regarding permission, write to Scholastic Inc. Attention: Permissions Department, 557 Broadway, New York, NY 10012.

ISBN 10: 0-545-06509-7
ISBN 13: 978-0-545-06509-2

Copyright © 2008 by Lynn Maslen Kertell. All rights reserved. Published by Scholastic Inc. by arrangement with Bob Books ® New Initiatives LLC. SCHOLASTIC and associated logos are trademarks and/or registered trademarks of Scholastic Inc. BOB BOOKS and MY FIRST BOB BOOKS are trademarks and/or registered trademarks of Bob Books Publications LLC.

30 29 28   21 22/0
Printed in China
First printing. August 2008

Fix It!

Matching and Sorting

by Lynn Maslen Kertell
pictures by Sue Hendra and John R. Maslen

Scholastic Inc.
New York • Toronto • London • Auckland • Sydney • Mexico City • New Delhi • Hong Kong • Buenos Aires

Sally and Seth were
going on a play date.

They went to Tanner's house.

Sally found a broken drum.
She asked Tanner's brother,
"Sam, can you fix it?"

What do they need to fix the drum?

5

Sam and Sally fixed the drum.

Seth's flag was broken.
"Can you fix it, Sam?" he asked.

"Sure," said Sam,
"what does it need?"

8

It needed a new stick.
"That should do it," said Seth.

Tanner's tricycle didn't work.
"What do we need to fix it?"
wondered Tanner.

"A new wheel!" yelled Tanner.
"That's just what it needed!"

Hooray! The toys were fixed
and everyone could play!

The Complete Bob Books® Series

READING READINESS

MY FIRST
BOB BOOKS ®
PRE-READING
SKILLS

MY FIRST
BOB BOOKS ®
ALPHABET

STAGE 1: STARTING TO READ

SET 1
BEGINNING
READERS

FIRST
STORIES

RHYMING
WORDS

STAGE 2: EMERGING READER

SET 2
ADVANCING
BEGINNERS

SIGHT WORDS
KINDERGARTEN

SIGHT WORDS
FIRST GRADE

STAGE 3: DEVELOPING READER

SET 3
WORD
FAMILIES

SET 4
COMPLEX
WORDS

SET 5
LONG
VOWELS

Lexile® Measure: AD340L
Guided Reading Level: G
Scholastic Reading Level: 1
Word Count: 103

Bob Books Apps
are available for
phones & tablets

www.BobBooks.com

Scholastic In
978-0-545-065

The Parade

Sorting and Classifying

My First
BOB
BOOKS

Hints About Sorting and Classifying

The items in this story are sorted using three criteria. Help your child find the correct item by breaking the task into steps: Search for the first criteria, then the second, and then the third. Learning to follow several steps is sophisticated thinking for a young child. As you read and reread the story, repetition will help him grasp the ideas.

Ask for Bob Books at your local bookstore, or visit www.bobbooks.com
No part of this publication may be reproduced, stored in a retrieval system, or transmitted in any form or by any means, electronic, mechanical, photocopying, recording, or otherwise, without written permission of the publisher. For information regarding permission, write to Scholastic Inc. Attention: Permissions Department, 557 Broadway, New York, NY 10012.

ISBN 10: 0-545-06510-0
ISBN 13: 978-0-545-06510-8

30 29 28   21 22/0
Printed in China
First printing. August 2008

The Parade

Sorting and Classifying

by Lynn Maslen Kertell
pictures by Sue Hendra and John R. Maslen

Scholastic Inc.

New York • Toronto • London • Auckland • Sydney • Mexico City • New Delhi • Hong Kong • Buenos Aires

The sun was shining on Parade Day.
Sally, Seth, and Tanner were excited.

They were going to march with
their favorite things.

Tanner liked the color blue.
He wanted to ride.

4

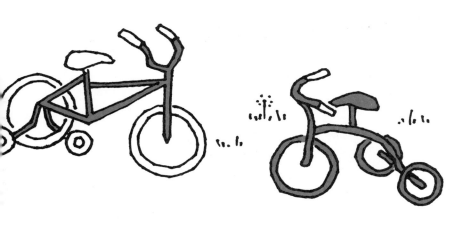

He adored things with three wheels.
What should he bring to the parade?

Tanner rode his tricycle.

Sally wanted something loud
and round. She loved to bang.

Sally chose a drum.

Seth felt happy. He wanted something tall and cheerful that waved in the breeze.

9

Seth picked a flag.

Rolling, banging, and fluttering,
the friends marched and marched.

11

It was the best parade ever!

The Complete Bob Books® Series

READING READINESS

MY FIRST
BOB BOOKS ®
PRE-READING
SKILLS

MY FIRST
BOB BOOKS ®
ALPHABET

STAGE 1: STARTING TO READ

SET 1
BEGINNING
READERS

FIRST
STORIES

RHYMING
WORDS

STAGE 2: EMERGING READER

SET 2
ADVANCING
BEGINNERS

SIGHT WORDS
KINDERGARTEN

SIGHT WORDS
FIRST GRADE

STAGE 3: DEVELOPING READER

SET 3
WORD
FAMILIES

SET 4
COMPLEX
WORDS

SET 5
LONG
VOWELS

Lexile® Measure: AD330L
Guided Reading Level: G
Scholastic Reading Level: 1
Word Count: 95

Bob Books Apps
are available for
phones & tablets

www.BobBooks.com

Scholastic In
978-0-545-06

Block Town

Learning Simple Patterns

SCHOLASTIC

Hints About Patterns

Seth and his brother Mac build a block pattern, but their friends
have trouble matching it. Help your child identify the pattern; then
let him decide whether Seth's friends have duplicated it correctly.
Your child's success, and the opportunity to teach you, builds
confidence and self-esteem.

Ask for Bob Books at your local bookstore, or visit www.bobbooks.com

No part of this publication may be reproduced, stored in a retrieval system, or transmitted in any form
or by any means, electronic, mechanical, photocopying, recording, or otherwise, without written
permission of the publisher. For information regarding permission, write to Scholastic Inc.
Attention: Permissions Department, 557 Broadway, New York, NY 10012.

ISBN 10: 0-545-06512-7
ISBN 13: 978-0-545-06512-2

30 29 28   21 22/0
Printed in China
First printing. August 2008

Block Town
Learning Simple Patterns

by Lynn Maslen Kertell
pictures by Sue Hendra and John R. Maslen

Scholastic Inc.
New York • Toronto • London • Auckland • Sydney • Mexico City • New Delhi • Hong Kong • Buenos Aires

Seth and Mac were building
a block town.

2

Block by block the town grew.
The blocks made a pattern.

Seth's friends wanted to
help build the block town.

4

ally and Tanner put blocks down, but
ne blocks didn't fit the pattern.

5

"Try another way," Seth suggested.

6

Sally and Tanner pushed
the blocks aside.

7

Sally and Tanner looked at the
scattered blocks. They did not give up

They turned the blocks upside down,
round and over. They kept on trying.

9

Seth had an idea. Together the
four friends looked at the shapes.

10

"Square, rectangle, rectangle!"
they said. "Now we can build."

Adding to the pattern, Sally, Tanner, and Seth built a fantastic block town

The Complete Bob Books® Series

READING READINESS

MY FIRST
BOB BOOKS ®
PRE-READING
SKILLS

MY FIRST
BOB BOOKS ®
ALPHABET

STAGE 1: STARTING TO READ

SET 1
BEGINNING
READERS

FIRST
STORIES

RHYMING
WORDS

STAGE 2: EMERGING READER

SET 2
ADVANCING
BEGINNERS

SIGHT WORDS
KINDERGARTEN

SIGHT WORDS
FIRST GRADE

STAGE 3: DEVELOPING READER

SET 3
WORD
FAMILIES

SET 4
COMPLEX
WORDS

SET 5
LONG
VOWELS

Lexile® Measure: AD450L
Guided Reading Level: G
Scholastic Reading Level: 2
Word Count: 113

Bob Books Apps
are available for
phones & tablets
www.BobBooks.com

Scholastic In
978-0-545-06

Three in a Row

Changing Patterns

Hints About Changing Patterns

Matryoshka (*ma-tr-YOsh-ka*) are sets of dolls that fit inside each other. They are also known as Russian nesting dolls. In this story, Sa and her friends are given matryoshkas and have fun setting up an then changing the patterns created by the dolls. Help your child use toys to create and then rearrange his own patterns.

Ask for Bob Books at your local bookstore, or visit www.bobbooks.com
No part of this publication may be reproduced, stored in a retrieval system, or transmitted in any form or by any means, electronic, mechanical, photocopying, recording, or otherwise, without written permission of the publisher. For information regarding permission, write to Scholastic Inc. Attention: Permissions Department, 557 Broadway, New York, NY 10012.

ISBN 10: 0-545-06515-1
ISBN 13: 978-0-545-06515-3

Copyright © 2008 by Lynn Maslen Kertell. All rights reserved. Published by Scholastic Inc. by arrangement with Bob Books ® New Initiatives LLC. SCHOLASTIC and associated logos are trademarks and/or registered trademarks of Scholastic Inc. BOB BOOKS and MY FIRST BOB BOOKS are trademarks and/or registered trademarks of Bob Books Publications LLC.

30 29 28   21 22/0
Printed in China
First printing. August 2008

Three in a Row

Changing Patterns

by Lynn Maslen Kertell
pictures by Sue Hendra and John R. Maslen

Scholastic Inc.
New York • Toronto • London • Auckland • Sydney • Mexico City • New Delhi • Hong Kong • Buenos Aires

Sally received a gift, a Russian
nesting doll called a matryoshka.

When she opened up her doll, there
was another one inside, and another.

3

Seth and Tanner received matryoshka
too. First Sally lined up her dolls.

4

Then Seth put his in a row.
Tanner lined up his dolls last.

5

The friends found another
way to line up their dolls.

Then they arranged the dolls
in a different pattern.

"Lets try this way," said Seth. Oops, one doll rolled under the couch.

Which one is missing?

9

"Where did Sally's matryoshka go?"
Tanner said to Seth.

"Who would like tea?"
asked Sally, rolling in a cart.

11

The matryoshkas' tea party
was a most elegant affair!

The Complete Bob Books® Series

READING READINESS

MY FIRST
BOB BOOKS®
PRE-READING
SKILLS

MY FIRST
BOB BOOKS®
ALPHABET

STAGE 1: STARTING TO READ

SET 1
BEGINNING
READERS

FIRST
STORIES

RHYMING
WORDS

STAGE 2: EMERGING READER

SET 2
ADVANCING
BEGINNERS

SIGHT WORDS
KINDERGARTEN

SIGHT WORDS
FIRST GRADE

STAGE 3: DEVELOPING READER

SET 3
WORD
FAMILIES

SET 4
COMPLEX
WORDS

SET 5
LONG
VOWELS

Lexile® Measure: AD490L
Guided Reading Level: I
Scholastic Reading Level: 2
Word Count: 113

Bob Books Apps
are available for
phones & tablets

www.BobBooks.com

Scholastic I
978-0-545-0

Snow

Building Complex Patterns

My First
BOB
BOOKS

Hints About More Complex Patterns

The patterns in this book grow in complexity as Seth plays in the snow. If your child is a kinetic learner, he or she will love moving in pattern: hop, hop, stomp! Explore the simplest patterns in the boo first, such as Seth's footprints. Once these are mastered, look for more complexity. Look for patterns in your own environment as we

ISBN 10: 0-545-06516-X
ISBN 13: 978-0-545-06516-0

30 29 28   21 22/0
Printed in China
First printing. August 2008

Snow
More Complex Patterns

by Lynn Maslen Kertell
pictures by Sue Hendra and John R. Maslen

Scholastic Inc.
New York • Toronto • London • Auckland • Sydney • Mexico City • New Delhi • Hong Kong • Buenos Aires

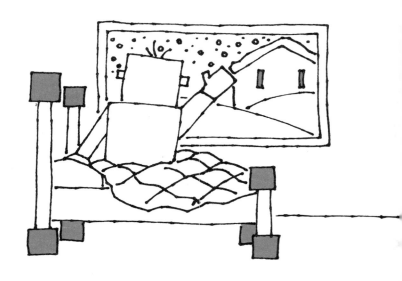

When Seth woke up, the
ground was covered with white.

The fence posts had white hats.
Seth bundled up in his warm
snowsuit to go outside.

Step, step, step, step. Seth's feet
made a pattern in the snow.

4

Hop, hop, hop, hop. Seth
could change the pattern.

5

Seth found a stick.
He made a new design.

Hop, drag, hop, drag.
Look at his pattern now!

7

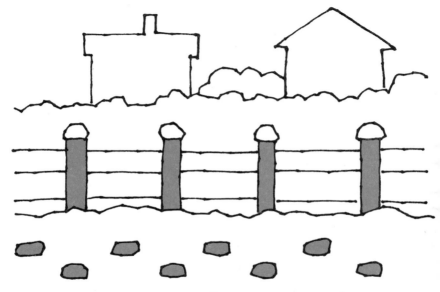

The caps of snow made
a pattern on the fence.

Whack! Seth changed the pattern!

9

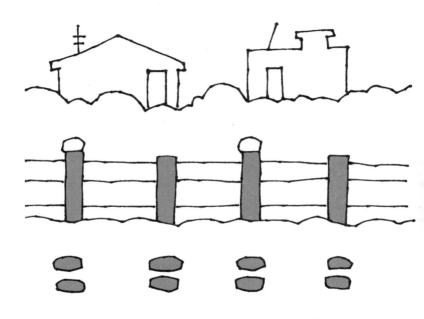

Jump, whack, jump, whack.

Jump, drag, jump, drag.

11

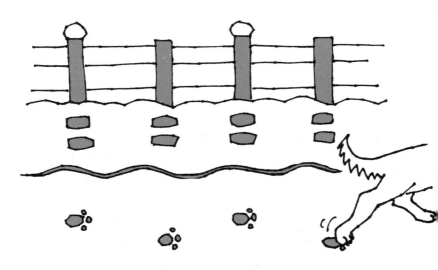

It is time to go home. Look what
Seth's dog did to his pattern!

The Complete Bob Books® Series

READING READINESS

MY FIRST
BOB BOOKS ®
PRE-READING
SKILLS

MY FIRST
BOB BOOKS ®
ALPHABET

STAGE 1: STARTING TO READ

SET 1
BEGINNING
READERS

FIRST
STORIES

RHYMING
WORDS

STAGE 2: EMERGING READER

SET 2
ADVANCING
BEGINNERS

SIGHT WORDS
KINDERGARTEN

SIGHT WORDS
FIRST GRADE

STAGE 3: DEVELOPING READER

SET 3
WORD
FAMILIES

SET 4
COMPLEX
WORDS

SET 5
LONG
VOWELS

 Bob Books Apps are available for phones & tablets

www.BobBooks.com

Lexile® Measure: AD390L
Guided Reading Level: G
Scholastic Reading Level: 1
Word Count: 102

Scholastic I
978-0-545-0

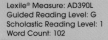

Get Ready!

Learning Simple Sequences

My First
BOB
BOOKS

Hints About Sequences

Kids love to play the *What's Next?* game. Making predictions also prepares kids for reading by teaching context and comprehension skills. Look at the pictures in the book for clues as to what will happen next. Then practice making predictions in everyday life. Before school or an outing to the park, empower your child by asking, "What should happen next?"

Ask for Bob Books at your local bookstore, or visit www.bobbooks.com

ISBN 10: 0-545-06517-8
ISBN 13: 978-0-545-06517-7

Copyright © 2008 by Lynn Maslen Kertell. All rights reserved. Published by Scholastic Inc. by arrangement with Bob Books ® New Initiatives LLC. SCHOLASTIC and associated logos are trademarks and/or registered trademarks of Scholastic Inc. BOB BOOKS and MY FIRST BOB BOOKS are trademarks and/or registered trademarks of Bob Books Publications LLC.

30 29 28   21 22/0
Printed in China
First printing. August 2008

Get Ready!

Learning Simple Sequences

by Lynn Maslen Kertell
pictures by Sue Hendra and John R. Maslen

Scholastic Inc.
New York • Toronto • London • Auckland • Sydney • Mexico City • New Delhi • Hong Kong • Buenos Aires

Tanner was eating his
lunch, but he was ready.

He was ready to play with his
toys! What happened next?

Tanner finished his lunch.
Then he jumped down to play.

Sally was getting ready – ready
to run! What happened next?

Sally put on her shoes. Then
she ran to Tanner's house!

6

Seth was getting ready – ready
to ride. What happened next?

Seth put on his helmet. Then he scooted to Tanner's house.

Sally and Seth arrived at Tanner's house. What happened next?

9

They knocked on the door.
"Hi, Sally. Hi, Seth!" shouted Tanner.

The three friends were ready
to play. What happened next?

11

They did play —
all the way until dinnertime.

The Complete Bob Books® Series

READING READINESS

MY FIRST
BOB BOOKS®
PRE-READING
SKILLS

MY FIRST
BOB BOOKS®
ALPHABET

STAGE 1: STARTING TO READ

SET 1
BEGINNING
READERS

FIRST
STORIES

RHYMING
WORDS

STAGE 2: EMERGING READER

SET 2
ADVANCING
BEGINNERS

SIGHT WORDS
KINDERGARTEN

SIGHT WORDS
FIRST GRADE

STAGE 3: DEVELOPING READER

SET 3
WORD
FAMILIES

SET 4
COMPLEX
WORDS

SET 5
LONG
VOWELS

Lexile® Measure: AD270L
Guided Reading Level: F
Scholastic Reading Level: 1
Word Count: 111

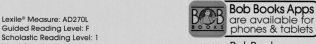

Bob Books Apps
are available for
phones & tablets

www.BobBooks.com

Scholastic
978-0-545-0

Guessing Machine

Predicting Sequences

My First BOB BOOKS

Hints About Context and Sequencing

This story contains a guessing game with a twist. The expected
happens; then the unexpected occurs. Use this book to encour
your children to tell their own stories. Let the unexpected carry y
children into flights of fancy.

Ask for Bob Books at your local bookstore, or visit www.bobbooks.com
No part of this publication may be reproduced, stored in a retrieval system, or transmitted in any form
or by any means, electronic, mechanical, photocopying, recording, or otherwise, without written
permission of the publisher. For information regarding permission, write to Scholastic Inc.
Attention: Permissions Department, 557 Broadway, New York, NY 10012.

ISBN 10: 0-545-06519-4
ISBN 13: 978-0-545-06519-1

Copyright © 2008 by Lynn Maslen Kertell. All rights reserved. Published by Scholastic Inc. by arrangement
with Bob Books ® New Initiatives LLC. SCHOLASTIC and associated logos are trademarks and/or registered
trademarks of Scholastic Inc. BOB BOOKS and MY FIRST BOB BOOKS are trademarks and/or registered
trademarks of Bob Books Publications LLC.

30 29 28   21 22/0
Printed in China
First printing. August 2008

The Guessing Machine

Predicting Sequences

by Lynn Maslen Kertell
pictures by Sue Hendra and John R. Maslen

Scholastic Inc.

New York • Toronto • London • Auckland • Sydney • Mexico City • New Delhi • Hong Kong • Buenos Aires

A Guessing Machine came to town.
What does a Guessing Machine do?

2

It guesses what comes
next. You can guess, too.

Seth started to stack the blocks.

You can guess with the Guessing
Machine. What happened next?

Did you guess that Seth
built a block tower? He did!

Here's a surprise! Then
Tanner knocked it down!

It was raining. Sally put on
her rain boots, coat, and hat.

Can you and the Guessing Machine
guess what happened next?

9

Did you guess that Sally went out
to play in the rain? She did!

urprise! Then the rain stopped. Seth
nd Tanner came out to play, too.

What did Sally, Seth, and
Tanner do next? Guess!

The Complete Bob Books® Series

READING READINESS

MY FIRST
BOB BOOKS ®
PRE-READING
SKILLS

MY FIRST
BOB BOOKS ®
ALPHABET

STAGE 1: STARTING TO READ

SET 1
BEGINNING
READERS

FIRST
STORIES

RHYMING
WORDS

STAGE 2: EMERGING READER

SET 2
ADVANCING
BEGINNERS

SIGHT WORDS
KINDERGARTEN

SIGHT WORDS
FIRST GRADE

STAGE 3: DEVELOPING READER

SET 3
WORD
FAMILIES

SET 4
COMPLEX
WORDS

SET 5
LONG
VOWELS

Lexile® Measure: AD260L
Guided Reading Level: G
Scholastic Reading Level: 1
Word Count: 114

Bob Books Apps
are available for
phones & tablets

www.BobBooks.com

Scholastic I
978-0-545-0

The Beach

Building Longer Sequences

SCHOLASTIC

My First
BOB
BOOKS

Hints About Longer Sequences

Sally and her friends want to go to the beach, but several things must happen first. Working through progressive steps builds cognitive skills in young learners, and recognizing context clues builds early reading success. Talk about what steps you and your child must take to go on vacation, to the grocery store, or to bed. What other activities take several steps of preparation?

Ask for Bob Books at your local bookstore, or visit www.bobbooks.com

No part of this publication may be reproduced, stored in a retrieval system, or transmitted in any form or by any means, electronic, mechanical, photocopying, recording, or otherwise, without written permission of the publisher. For information regarding permission, write to Scholastic Inc. Attention: Permissions Department, 557 Broadway, New York, NY 10012.

ISBN 10: 0-545-06520-8
ISBN 13: 978-0-545-06520-7

30 29 28   21 22/0
Printed in China
First printing. August 2008

The Beach

Building Longer Sequences

by Lynn Maslen Kertell
pictures by Sue Hendra and John R. Maslen

Scholastic Inc.

New York • Toronto • London • Auckland • Sydney • Mexico City • New Delhi • Hong Kong • Buenos Aires

"Who wants to go to the beach?"
asked Sally.

2

"I do, I do, I do!"
shouted her friends.

3

"What is the first thing we need to do?"
asked Sally.

4

"Pack snacks," said Tanner.
"Remember towels," said Dot.

"We're packed!" said Sally.
"What's next?"

6

"Put on sunscreen and swimsuits,"
said Seth.

"I'm done," said Sally. "Now what is nex
"Hop in the car," said Mat. "Let's go!"

8

They buckled up and
drove to the beach.

"We know what we want to
do next!" shouted Tanner.

"Jump in the water!" said Sally.

Thank goodness they had nothing else
do but play all day in the sparkling su

The Complete Bob Books® Series

READING READINESS

MY FIRST
BOB BOOKS®
PRE-READING
SKILLS

MY FIRST
BOB BOOKS®
ALPHABET

STAGE 1: STARTING TO READ

SET 1
BEGINNING
READERS

FIRST
STORIES

RHYMING
WORDS

STAGE 2: EMERGING READER

SET 2
ADVANCING
BEGINNERS

SIGHT WORDS
KINDERGARTEN

SIGHT WORDS
FIRST GRADE

STAGE 3: DEVELOPING READER

SET 3
WORD
FAMILIES

SET 4
COMPLEX
WORDS

SET 5
LONG
VOWELS

Lexile® Measure: AD330L
Guided Reading Level: G
Scholastic Reading Level: 1
Word Count: 106

 Bob Books Apps
are available for
phones & tablets

www.BobBooks.com

Scholastic
978-0-545-0